FROM THE APPLE TO THE MOON

FROM THE APPLE TO THE MOON

Written and illustrated by
ANNIE VALLOTTON

 ABINGDON PRESS Nashville • New York

FROM THE APPLE TO THE MOON

ISBN 0-687-13633-4

Library of Congress Catalog Card Number: 79-130358

SET UP, PRINTED, AND BOUND BY THE
PARTHENON PRESS, AT NASHVILLE,
TENNESSEE, UNITED STATES OF AMERICA

Why the death of children?
Why the torture of the innocent?
Why suffering?
Why hunger?
Why war?
If there is a God—why? Why?
Who among us has not said or thought such things in a troubled moment?
Here is a simple walk through the story of man—
a few brushstrokes, a few spots of color, a few words.
Do they answer your questions—
or lead to more question marks?
Surely our walk on the earth must have meaning . . .
But what is it? Do you know?

At the dawn of time God the Spirit creates
the planet Earth in the vastness of space—

There he brings forth life.

In a marvelous garden
he places a particle of his Spirit in two special creatures:
man and woman.

They are entirely free, except that . . .

. . . one tree is forbidden,
the tree bearing the fruit of knowledge.

With them in the garden is the Evil Spirit,
who urges them to eat the fruit.
"Eat, and you will become equals of the creative Spirit!"
They taste it.

For this act of disobedience
God the Spirit drives man and woman from the garden.

They are now faced with a lifetime of choices:
between good and evil, right and wrong, beauty and ugliness.

They,
their children,
and their children's children,
led by their selfishness,
begin to quarrel and fight.

But the Spirit continues to dwell among them.

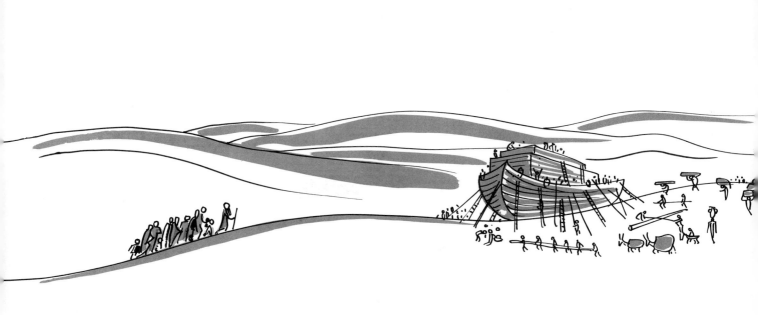

Finally, the Spirit chooses a man who has remained close to him and orders the man to build a huge boat as a refuge for himself and his family . . .

. . . as well as for two of every species of animal.

No sooner is this order fulfilled
than floods of water cover the earth.
Only those on the boat are spared.

When the water recedes and the land reappears, the man and his family and all the animals come out of the boat. The rainbow is a sign that the Spirit remains with them.

Little by little Earth is repopulated, and men,
caught again by pride, start erecting a tower.

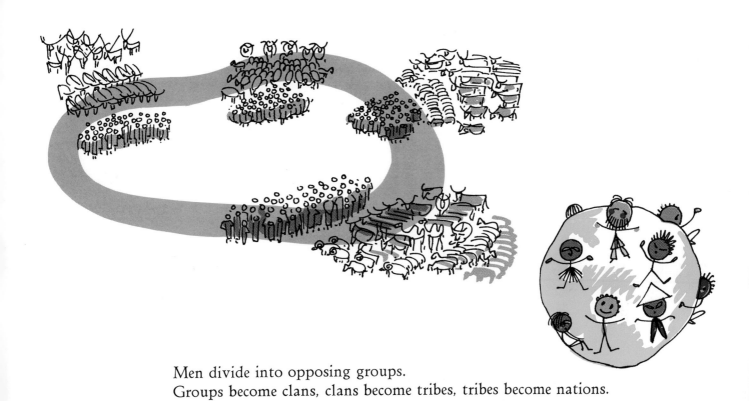

Men divide into opposing groups.
Groups become clans, clans become tribes, tribes become nations.

King follows king; one civilization another.
There are yellow kings, gurus, mandarins, learned men;

copper-colored kings, astronomers, diviners;
revered kings, lamas, buddhas.

There are kings who build enormous tombs and monuments; astrologers, kings who hunt tigers;

kings who patronize arts; orators; philosophers;
kings who are builders of roads; conquerors; merchants . . .
AND ALWAYS THERE ARE WARS!

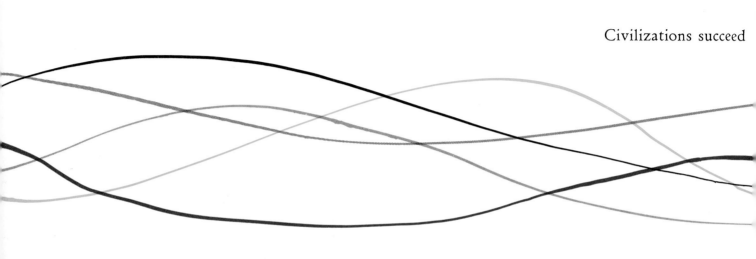

Civilizations succeed

Yet men do not change.
They remain envious and proud.

one another and pass away . . .

Into this world the Spirit sends his own son
to teach men of his love.
Humble shepherds and learned astrologers come to worship him.

This son of God lives among men, healing the sick and teaching a new way of life. God loves them, and because they possess a particle of his Spirit, they must love their neighbors.

God loves them so much he gives his son's life.
Men put the son on a cross where he dies, suffering as a man.
But three days later, as he had told his followers,
he rises from the dead as the Son of God.

After his victory over death, his companions go throughout the world
proclaiming all they have seen and heard and healing the sick.

Evil remains strong on the Earth.
Hordes continue to ravage the lands.

The Son's followers organize and become
very powerful.

Men by the thousands leave their homes
to wrest from unbelievers
the empty tomb of the Son of the Spirit.

Others, to praise the Spirit, erect imposing buildings,
refuges where they pray, study, and copy sacred scriptures.

Fearless navigators discover new lands.

A scholar prints texts for the first time.
Ideas, theories, the code of life spread over the Earth.

Having rediscovered the truth taught by the Son of the Spirit,
a few men choose to testify to this truth. Many follow them.
In the name of the truth which each believes he alone holds,
wars begin again.

Through it all the arts flourish.

Music lends grace to morals and manners.

The parade of leaders goes on.
Some are great, some magnificent, some terrible—and some are numbered.

More abuses.
Heavy taxes on the poor; too many privileges for the great.
Men rebel, seize power, and proclaim a bill of rights.
A great idea sinks in anarchy.

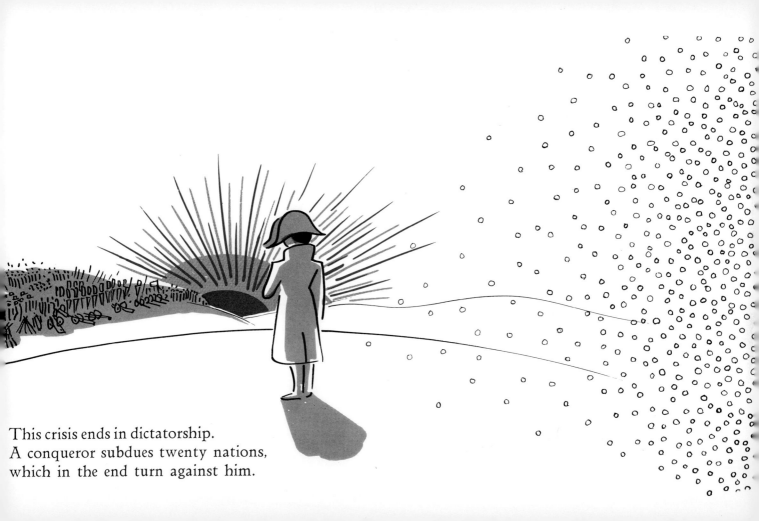

This crisis ends in dictatorship.
A conqueror subdues twenty nations,
which in the end turn against him.

Periods of war, periods of peace.

Men invent all kinds of machinery.

Scientists master mysterious forces, which in turn dominate them.

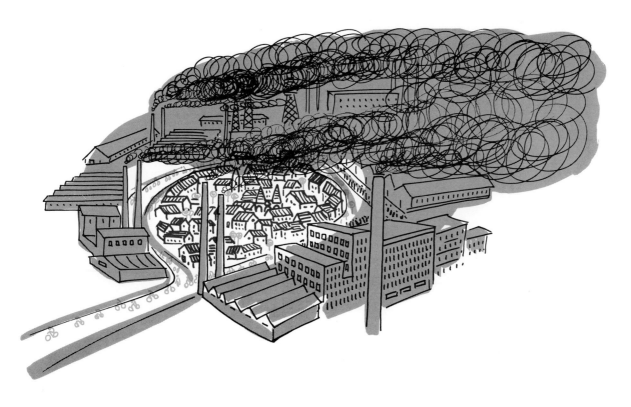

Men leave their villages and farms for the cities.

The well-being of men is taken into consideration. They are looked after, educated, entertained, cared for spiritually.

Men are interested in everything.
Crowds gather in dark halls to watch moving pictures
. . . and to dream.

Women also are dissatisfied and speak out.
They begin to assume responsibilities . . . at last!

In order to frighten and dominate others,
men devise more weapons, and once again are led to total war.
The Evil Spirit dominates them.

The innocent suffer and die.

Horrors exceed all bounds.
  Treasures vanish away:
cathedrals, saucepans, letters, customs . . . little odds and ends.

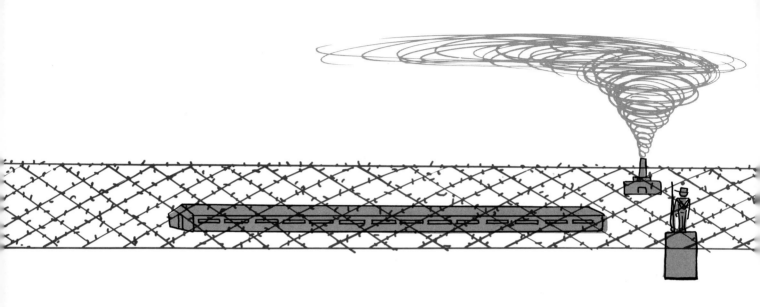

Populations are imprisoned, tortured,
systematically reduced to nothing.

In spite of wars, overcrowding becomes an alarming problem. Shortages threaten men. Responsible authorities are preoccupied on a worldwide scale.

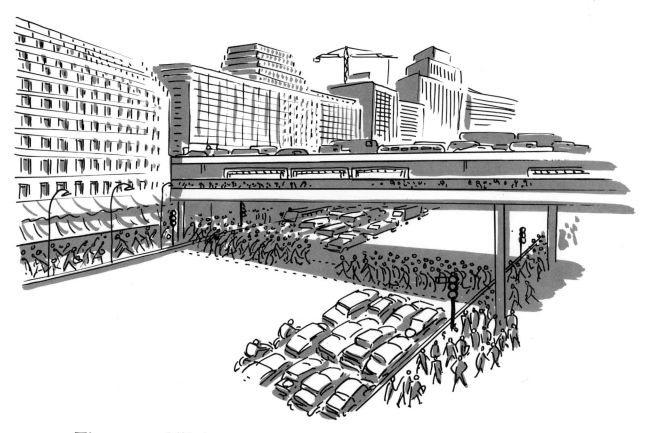

The tempo of life increases.
Men dare not stop for fear of losing time or advantage.

Men live with the aim of amusing themselves.
They pour out tremendous amounts of energy and talent.

Vacations for all, even cramped together.

Courageous men visit the bottom of the sea.

And others explore

grottoes and caverns.

Daring men

climb the highest mountains.

Sports of all kinds everywhere.

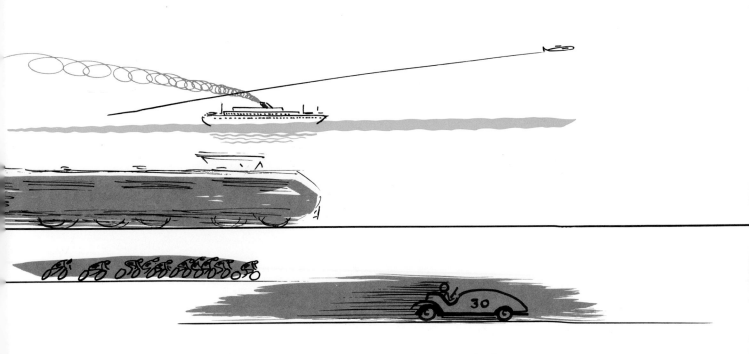

Men go faster, higher, and farther than ever before.

Public opinion is recognized as important
and is influenced by fair means or foul.

Starvation on one hand . . .

. . . on the other hand, superabundance and luxury,
readily available on the installment plan.

Surrounded by free riches, men care only
for those things that have price tags.
They have lost the ability to notice and marvel.

Man becomes more and more intoxicated.
Noise, idle talk, tranquilizers, stimulants,
alcohol, schemes—
All drive him farther away from the Spirit.

What chaos!

Youth shakes off bonds.

So do nations.

Racial tensions grow into violence.

Congresses, conferences, round tables, councils . . .
in the name of the Spirit!

Man chokes
his particle of Spirit.
He makes of it a dry onion
when it could be
a sparkling flame.

But here and there the Spirit does discern a few glimmers of hope:
an unselfish deed, a smile, a little tenderness, some forgiveness . . .

The Spirit sees the young people and rejoices.

Here and there
he sees the hearts of men being reached . . .

. . . gestures of concern

. . . men
who oppose violence with calmness

. . . men
helping others
to help themselves.

He sees the faces of worldwide cooperation.

But too many men are lost in their own problems:
economic, agricultural, academic, religious.
There is little communication.

Instead, monologues of withered words!

Controversies...strikes...rebellions...revolutions.

Men
desperately
seek meaning
in their regimented,
computerized society.

They fear a future dominated by robots and Big Brother.

To increase their prestige and knowledge,
they travel to the moon.

And what next?

Man has tasted the apple to obtain freedom . . .

He has left the earth
to reach the moon . . .

To obtain knowledge?

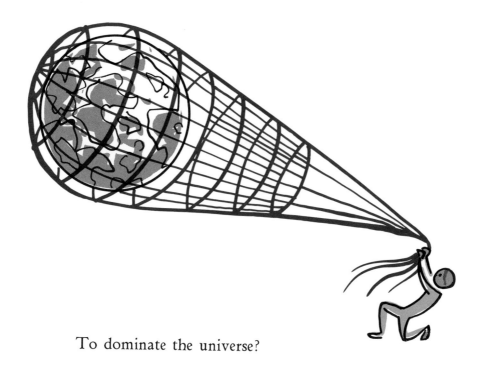

To dominate the universe?

To escape from himself?

Or does he seek
to avoid the Spirit,
the Creator of all things . . .

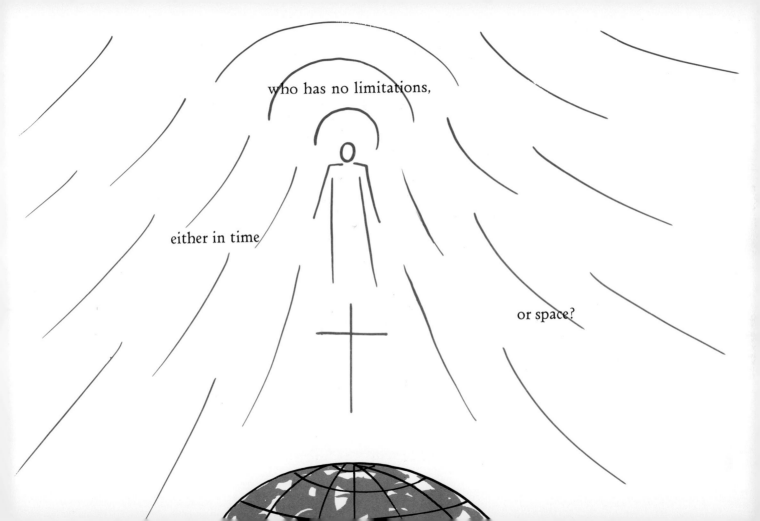

Could man's greatest discovery be
the choice of life with the Spirit?

The acceptance of a gift
freely offered?

To accept the Spirit
is to accept life . . .

for the Spirit *is* life.

Man is free to choose.